MW00697655

I'm Perfectly Imperfect

Created, published, and distributed by Knock Knock
11111 Jefferson Blvd. #5167
Culver City, CA 90231
knockknockstuff.com
Knock Knock is a registered trademark of Knock Knock LLC
Inner-Truth is a registered trademark of Knock Knock LLC

Made in China

ISBN: 978-1-68349-270-2
UPC: 825703-50195-7

10 9 8 7 6 5 4 3 2 1

HELLO, YOU.

Good you. Not-so-good you. Messy you. Sensitive you. Sad, happy, beautiful you. Weirdo you. Boring you. Freaking out and sometimes secretly jealous you. Doubtful, brave, bold you. Hopeful, anxious, big-hearted you. Every bit of you has its time, story, purpose, and place in your life. (Even if you eventually outgrow or lovingly leave some of them behind.) Together, they're what makes you utterly and uniquely, perfectly and imperfectly Y-O-U.

Okay sure, so you've made some mistakes here and there. Big ones? Probably, at least a few. Little ones? Lots of 'em. But here's the thing: sometimes that's what makes us beautiful. And it's certainly what makes us human. Either way, we still gotta figure out how to love and accept ourselves. Otherwise, what's the point?

Luckily, this journal is here to help with that.

As celebrated self-help author Deepak Chopra claims, "Journaling is one of the most powerful tools we have to transform our lives." In addition to helping put one's mind at ease, journal writing has been shown to aid physical health. According to a widely cited study by James W. Pennebaker and Janel D. Seagal, "Writing about important personal experiences in an emotional way . . . Brings about improvements in mental and physical health." Proven benefits include better stress management, strengthened immune systems, fewer doctor visits, and improvement in chronic illnesses such as asthma. (Between the self-actualization and the journaling, you'll be patting yourself on the back in no time.)

It's not entirely clear how journaling accomplishes all this. Catharsis is involved, but many also note the value of organizing experiences into a cohesive narrative. According to *Newsweek*, some experts believe that journaling "forces us to transform the ruminations cluttering our minds into coherent stories." Writing about your life can help you clarify who you are and how you can nurture your true, best, perfectly imperfect self.

For most of us, rock-solid self-worth, self-acceptance, and self-love don't come easy. Learning to embrace yourself in all your sloppy, human glory takes work. It's a process, much like keeping a journal. Specialists agree that in order to reap the benefits of journaling you have to stick with it, quasi-daily, for as little as five minutes at a time (at least fifteen minutes, however, is best), even on days when you feel over it, exhausted, or impossibly broken. Finding regular writing times and comfortable locations can help with consistency.

So, what should you write about? Why, you, of course! (At least to start.) Unleash yourself on the page. Document your strengths and your charms, as well as your flaws and weaknesses. Double high-five your "best-you" moments, and bow to your worst. You can also write about other folks, all those perfectly imperfect people who seem to inspire or vex you most. Write about your days, weeks, months, years—and moments, both little and big. Write about times when you really felt seen and loved, by yourself or by someone else.

Use the quotes inside this journal as a jumping-off point for observations and explorations. Don't self-censor or edit. Journaling is a means of reflection, not a structured composition. In other words, just let whatever flows flow, and feel . . . free. Follow your gut (unless it tells you to do something really dumb), open your mind, and keep writing. Stop second-guessing yourself. Start taking baby steps toward self-liberation, and let go of any nagging fear that you're too much—or too little. Radically accept yourself. Make space to grow and evolve. Give yourself love. And then share that love with others.

Finally, find a special spot for your journal so it'll be easy to find whether you're feeling like a peacock or are stuck in bed, trapped in a shame vortex. Keep it near your freak flag, if that's your thing. Or don't! Just do, be, and celebrate you. That's what these pages are meant for.

I myself am made entirely of flaws, stitched together with good intentions.

DATE:

How I'm Embracing My Perfectly Imperfect Self Today:

LEVEL OF SELF-ACCEPTANCE TODAY:

☐ A- ☐ A ☐ A+ ☐ A++

I have been bent and broken, but—I hope—into a better shape.

DATE:

How I'm Embracing My Perfectly Imperfect Self Today:

LEVEL OF SELF-ACCEPTANCE TODAY:

☐ A- ☐ A ☐ A+ ☐ A++

No need to hurry. No need to sparkle. No need to be anyone but oneself.

DATE:

How I'm Embracing My Perfectly Imperfect Self Today:

LEVEL OF SELF-ACCEPTANCE TODAY:

☐ A- ☐ A ☐ A+ ☐ A++

Sometimes the thing that's weird about you is the thing that's cool about you.

DATE:

How I'm Embracing My Perfectly Imperfect Self Today:

LEVEL OF SELF-ACCEPTANCE TODAY:

☐ A- ☐ A ☐ A+ ☐ A++

Accept who you are. Unless you're a serial killer.

DATE:

How I'm Embracing My Perfectly Imperfect Self Today:

LEVEL OF SELF-ACCEPTANCE TODAY:

☐ A- ☐ A ☐ A+ ☐ A++

Not all those who wander are lost.

DATE:

How I'm Embracing My Perfectly Imperfect Self Today:

LEVEL OF SELF-ACCEPTANCE TODAY:

☐ **A-** ☐ **A** ☐ **A+** ☐ **A++**

It is a serious thing just to be alive on this fresh morning in the broken world.

DATE:

How I'm Embracing My Perfectly Imperfect Self Today:

LEVEL OF SELF-ACCEPTANCE TODAY:

☐ A- ☐ A ☐ A+ ☐ A++

and here you are living despite it all

DATE:

How I'm Embracing My Perfectly Imperfect Self Today:

LEVEL OF SELF-ACCEPTANCE TODAY:

☐ A- ☐ A ☐ A+ ☐ A++

Anything we don't like, we'll turn it into a happy little tree or something; we don't make mistakes, we just have happy accidents.

DATE:

How I'm Embracing My Perfectly Imperfect Self Today:

LEVEL OF SELF-ACCEPTANCE TODAY:

☐ A- ☐ A ☐ A+ ☐ A++

Owning up to your vulnerabilities is a form of strength.

DATE:

How I'm Embracing My Perfectly Imperfect Self Today:

LEVEL OF SELF-ACCEPTANCE TODAY:

☐ A- ☐ A ☐ A+ ☐ A++

Sometimes if you expose your vulnerability, someone else will feel comforted. It's like we're all in this boat together.

DATE:

How I'm Embracing My Perfectly Imperfect Self Today:

LEVEL OF SELF-ACCEPTANCE TODAY:

☐ A- ☐ A ☐ A+ ☐ A++

For whatever we lose (like a you or a me)

it's always ourselves we find in the sea

DATE:

How I'm Embracing My Perfectly Imperfect Self Today:

LEVEL OF SELF-ACCEPTANCE TODAY:

☐ A- ☐ A ☐ A+ ☐ A++

Out beyond ideas of wrongdoing and rightdoing there is a field. I'll meet you there.

DATE:

How I'm Embracing My Perfectly Imperfect Self Today:

LEVEL OF SELF-ACCEPTANCE TODAY:

☐ A- ☐ A ☐ A+ ☐ A++

I am running away from my responsibilities. And it feels good.

DATE:

How I'm Embracing My Perfectly Imperfect Self Today:

LEVEL OF SELF-ACCEPTANCE TODAY:

☐ A-　☐ A　☐ A+　☐ A++

I don't like people who have never fallen or stumbled. Their virtue is lifeless and of little value. Life hasn't revealed its beauty to them.

DATE:

How I'm Embracing My Perfectly Imperfect Self Today:

LEVEL OF SELF-ACCEPTANCE TODAY:

☐ A- ☐ A ☐ A+ ☐ A++

I have woven a parachute out of everything broken.

DATE:

How I'm Embracing My Perfectly Imperfect Self Today:

LEVEL OF SELF-ACCEPTANCE TODAY:

☐ A- ☐ A ☐ A+ ☐ A++

One of the basic rules of the universe is that nothing is perfect. Perfection simply doesn't exist . . . Without imperfection, neither you nor I would exist.

DATE:

How I'm Embracing My Perfectly Imperfect Self Today:

LEVEL OF SELF-ACCEPTANCE TODAY:

☐ A-   ☐ A   ☐ A+   ☐ A++

A jewel's just a rock put under enormous heat and pressure.

DATE:

How I'm Embracing My Perfectly Imperfect Self Today:

LEVEL OF SELF-ACCEPTANCE TODAY:

☐ A- ☐ A ☐ A+ ☐ A++

I'm not okay, you're not okay, and that's okay.

DATE:

How I'm Embracing My Perfectly Imperfect Self Today:

LEVEL OF SELF-ACCEPTANCE TODAY:

☐ A- ☐ A ☐ A+ ☐ A++

And once it was proposed to me that it was all right to be like I am, I finally quit apologizing for it.

DATE:

How I'm Embracing My Perfectly Imperfect Self Today:

LEVEL OF SELF-ACCEPTANCE TODAY:

☐ A-　☐ A　☐ A+　☐ A++

You are part of the universe; you are made of stars.

DATE:

How I'm Embracing My Perfectly Imperfect Self Today:

LEVEL OF SELF-ACCEPTANCE TODAY:

☐ A-　☐ A　☐ A+　☐ A++

It's time to take better care of yourself, to embrace and support yourself more . . . and to make better judgments about who is worthy of the full, glorious light of weirdness you will someday shine on the world, far and wide.

DATE:

How I'm Embracing My Perfectly Imperfect Self Today:

LEVEL OF SELF-ACCEPTANCE TODAY:

☐ A- ☐ A ☐ A+ ☐ A++

She has often felt that her outsides were too dull for her insides, that deep within her there was something better than what everyone else could see.

DATE:

How I'm Embracing My Perfectly Imperfect Self Today:

LEVEL OF SELF-ACCEPTANCE TODAY:

☐ A- ☐ A ☐ A+ ☐ A++

We begin to find and become ourselves when we notice how we are already found, already truly, entirely, wildly, messily, marvelously who we were born to be.

DATE:

How I'm Embracing My Perfectly Imperfect Self Today:

LEVEL OF SELF-ACCEPTANCE TODAY:

☐ A- ☐ A ☐ A+ ☐ A++

It's a liberating feeling when you realize I'm still here; I still wake up every day; I still have the opportunity to do some good.

DATE:

How I'm Embracing My Perfectly Imperfect Self Today:

LEVEL OF SELF-ACCEPTANCE TODAY:

☐ A-   ☐ A   ☐ A+   ☐ A++

We are flawed creatures, all of us. Some of us think that means we should fix our flaws. But get rid of my flaws and there would be no one left.

DATE:

How I'm Embracing My Perfectly Imperfect Self Today:

LEVEL OF SELF-ACCEPTANCE TODAY:

☐ A- ☐ A ☐ A+ ☐ A++

Follow your inner moonlight; don’t hide the madness.

DATE:

How I'm Embracing My Perfectly Imperfect Self Today:

LEVEL OF SELF-ACCEPTANCE TODAY:

☐ A- ☐ A ☐ A+ ☐ A++

Look at that tree growing up there out of that grating. It gets no sun, and water only when it rains. It's growing out of sour earth. And it's strong because its hard struggle to live is making it strong.

DATE:

How I'm Embracing My Perfectly Imperfect Self Today:

LEVEL OF SELF-ACCEPTANCE TODAY:

☐ **A-** ☐ **A** ☐ **A+** ☐ **A++**

Imperfections are not inadequacies; they are reminders that we're all in this together.

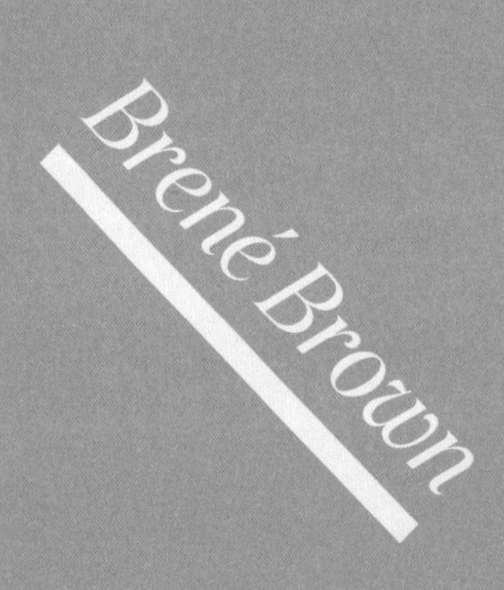

DATE:

How I'm Embracing My Perfectly Imperfect Self Today:

LEVEL OF SELF-ACCEPTANCE TODAY:

☐ A- ☐ A ☐ A+ ☐ A++

"Well, I am pretty," replied Charlotte. "There's no denying that. Almost all spiders are rather nice-looking. I'm not as flashy as some, but I'll do."

DATE:

How I'm Embracing My Perfectly Imperfect Self Today:

LEVEL OF SELF-ACCEPTANCE TODAY:

☐ A- ☐ A ☐ A+ ☐ A++

She was becoming herself and daily casting aside that fictitious self which we assume like a garment with which to appear before the world.

DATE:

How I'm Embracing My Perfectly Imperfect Self Today:

LEVEL OF SELF-ACCEPTANCE TODAY:

☐ A- ☐ A ☐ A+ ☐ A++

Nothing is accomplished without making fools of ourselves.

DATE:

How I'm Embracing My Perfectly Imperfect Self Today:

LEVEL OF SELF-ACCEPTANCE TODAY:

☐ A- ☐ A ☐ A+ ☐ A++

Forget your perfect offering
There is a crack in everything
That's how the light gets in.

DATE:

How I'm Embracing My Perfectly Imperfect Self Today:

LEVEL OF SELF-ACCEPTANCE TODAY:

☐ A- ☐ A ☐ A+ ☐ A++

I can finally see that all the terrible parts of my life, the embarrassing parts, the incidents I wanted to pretend never happened, and the things that make me "weird" and "different," were actually the most important parts of my life. They were the parts that made me me.

DATE:

How I'm Embracing My Perfectly Imperfect Self Today:

LEVEL OF SELF-ACCEPTANCE TODAY:

☐ A- ☐ A ☐ A+ ☐ A++

No one is without their difficulties, whether in high or low life, & every person knows best where their own shoe pinches.

DATE:

How I'm Embracing My Perfectly Imperfect Self Today:

LEVEL OF SELF-ACCEPTANCE TODAY:

☐ **A-** ☐ **A** ☐ **A+** ☐ **A++**

I prefer to be true to myself, even at the hazard of incurring the ridicule of others, rather than to be false, and incur my own abhorrence.

DATE:

How I'm Embracing My Perfectly Imperfect Self Today:

LEVEL OF SELF-ACCEPTANCE TODAY:

☐ A- ☐ A ☐ A+ ☐ A++

What and how much had I lost by trying to do only what was expected of me instead of what I myself had wished to do?

DATE:

How I'm Embracing My Perfectly Imperfect Self Today:

LEVEL OF SELF-ACCEPTANCE TODAY:

☐ A- ☐ A ☐ A+ ☐ A++

Confidence is 10% hard work and 90% delusion.

DATE:

How I'm Embracing My Perfectly Imperfect Self Today:

LEVEL OF SELF-ACCEPTANCE TODAY:

☐ A- ☐ A ☐ A+ ☐ A++

We guess. We may be wrong, but we take leap after leap in the dark.

DATE:

How I'm Embracing My Perfectly Imperfect Self Today:

LEVEL OF SELF-ACCEPTANCE TODAY:

☐ A- ☐ A ☐ A+ ☐ A++

Imperfection inspires invention, imagination, creativity. It stimulates. The more I feel imperfect, the more I feel alive.

DATE:

How I'm Embracing My Perfectly Imperfect Self Today:

LEVEL OF SELF-ACCEPTANCE TODAY:

☐ A- ☐ A ☐ A+ ☐ A++

These are the happiest moments of your life—when the real you comes out, when you don't care about the past and you don't worry about the future.

DATE:

How I'm Embracing My Perfectly Imperfect Self Today:

LEVEL OF SELF-ACCEPTANCE TODAY:

☐ A- ☐ A ☐ A+ ☐ A++

We're just all made of molecules and we're hurtling through space right now.

DATE:

How I'm Embracing My Perfectly Imperfect Self Today:

LEVEL OF SELF-ACCEPTANCE TODAY:

☐ **A-** ☐ **A** ☐ **A+** ☐ **A++**

Sometimes I tell myself, when I'm dealing with annoying adults, to picture the kid there. Because no matter how annoying the kid is, I can feel compassion for him or her.

DATE:

How I'm Embracing My Perfectly Imperfect Self Today:

LEVEL OF SELF-ACCEPTANCE TODAY:

☐ A- ☐ A ☐ A+ ☐ A++

I do think imperfection is underrated.

DATE:

How I'm Embracing My Perfectly Imperfect Self Today:

LEVEL OF SELF-ACCEPTANCE TODAY:

☐ A-　☐ A　☐ A+　☐ A++

It always felt like I was on an operating table and the anesthesia never worked.

DATE:

How I'm Embracing My Perfectly Imperfect Self Today:

LEVEL OF SELF-ACCEPTANCE TODAY:

☐ A- ☐ A ☐ A+ ☐ A++

I'm a little lost and confused and sensitive and insecure sometimes and that's all right with me because I'm pretty sure that's just what it means to be HUMAN.

DATE:

How I'm Embracing My Perfectly Imperfect Self Today:

LEVEL OF SELF-ACCEPTANCE TODAY:

☐ A- ☐ A ☐ A+ ☐ A++

Facing darkness is always really uncomfortable. It's better to go into the suffering and figure out what it really feels like instead of being afraid of it. This emotional pain is what binds us all.

DATE:

How I'm Embracing My Perfectly Imperfect Self Today:

LEVEL OF SELF-ACCEPTANCE TODAY:

☐ A- ☐ A ☐ A+ ☐ A++

I just look at women sometimes and I just want to ask them, “Do you know how fabulous you are?”

DATE:

How I'm Embracing My Perfectly Imperfect Self Today:

LEVEL OF SELF-ACCEPTANCE TODAY:

☐ A- ☐ A ☐ A+ ☐ A++

I love that I have learned to trust people with my heart, even if it will get broken.

DATE:

How I'm Embracing My Perfectly Imperfect Self Today:

LEVEL OF SELF-ACCEPTANCE TODAY:

☐ A- ☐ A ☐ A+ ☐ A++

I am who I am, doing what I came to do.

DATE:

How I'm Embracing My Perfectly Imperfect Self Today:

LEVEL OF SELF-ACCEPTANCE TODAY:

☐ A- ☐ A ☐ A+ ☐ A++

I know I'm an acquired taste. I'm anchovies.

DATE:

How I'm Embracing My Perfectly Imperfect Self Today:

LEVEL OF SELF-ACCEPTANCE TODAY:

☐ A- ☐ A ☐ A+ ☐ A++

Miracles happen all the time. We're here, aren't we?

DATE:

How I'm Embracing My Perfectly Imperfect Self Today:

LEVEL OF SELF-ACCEPTANCE TODAY:

☐ A- ☐ A ☐ A+ ☐ A++

I like my neuroses. I like knowing that they are real and that they are from my ancestors, that I have inherited them and that they are genetic.

DATE:

How I'm Embracing My Perfectly Imperfect Self Today:

LEVEL OF SELF-ACCEPTANCE TODAY:

☐ A- ☐ A ☐ A+ ☐ A++

You ARE YOU! And, now isn't that pleasant!

DATE:

How I'm Embracing My Perfectly Imperfect Self Today:

LEVEL OF SELF-ACCEPTANCE TODAY:

☐ A-　☐ A　☐ A+　☐ A++

I'll never be at such ease that I don't have something to write about. It's just one continuous meltdown.

DATE:

How I'm Embracing My Perfectly Imperfect Self Today:

LEVEL OF SELF-ACCEPTANCE TODAY:

☐ A- ☐ A ☐ A+ ☐ A++

I fell off my pink cloud with a thud.

DATE:

How I'm Embracing My Perfectly Imperfect Self Today:

LEVEL OF SELF-ACCEPTANCE TODAY:

☐ A- ☐ A ☐ A+ ☐ A++

I don't mean to be so sensitive, but that's just who I am. And I'm not afraid to admit it.

DATE:

How I'm Embracing My Perfectly Imperfect Self Today:

LEVEL OF SELF-ACCEPTANCE TODAY:

☐ A- ☐ A ☐ A+ ☐ A++

Accept who you are and revel in that.

DATE:

How I'm Embracing My Perfectly Imperfect Self Today:

LEVEL OF SELF-ACCEPTANCE TODAY:

☐ A- ☐ A ☐ A+ ☐ A++

No one is more dangerously insane than one who is sane all the time: he is like a steel bridge without flexibility, and the order of his life is rigid and brittle.

DATE:

How I'm Embracing My Perfectly Imperfect Self Today:

LEVEL OF SELF-ACCEPTANCE TODAY:

☐ A- ☐ A ☐ A+ ☐ A++

Once I had asked God for one or two extra inches in height, but instead he made me as tall as the sky, so high that I could not measure myself.

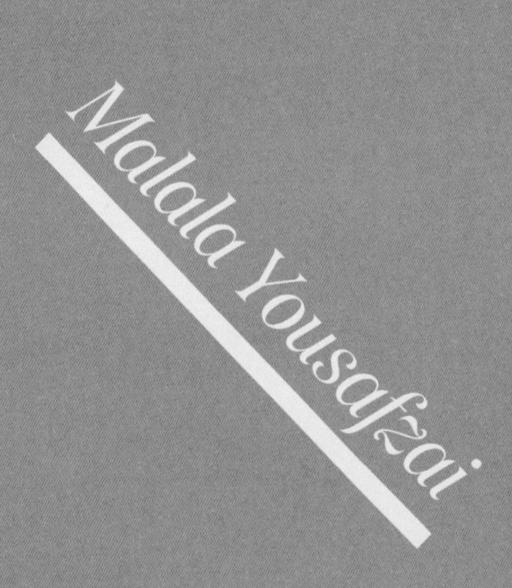

DATE:

How I'm Embracing My Perfectly Imperfect Self Today:

LEVEL OF SELF-ACCEPTANCE TODAY:

☐ A- ☐ A ☐ A+ ☐ A++

Insult my sexual prowess, my intellect, but not my pancakes.

DATE:

How I'm Embracing My Perfectly Imperfect Self Today:

LEVEL OF SELF-ACCEPTANCE TODAY:

☐ A- ☐ A ☐ A+ ☐ A++

We are all stinking messes, every last one of us, or we once were messes and found our way out, or we are trying to find our way out of a mess, scratching, reaching.

DATE:

How I'm Embracing My Perfectly Imperfect Self Today:

LEVEL OF SELF-ACCEPTANCE TODAY:

☐ A- ☐ A ☐ A+ ☐ A++

Like a fish which swims calmly in deep water, I felt all about me the secure supporting pressure of my own life. Ragged, inglorious, and apparently purposeless, but my own.

DATE:

How I'm Embracing My Perfectly Imperfect Self Today:

LEVEL OF SELF-ACCEPTANCE TODAY:

☐ A- ☐ A ☐ A+ ☐ A++

I'm me, and I like that there are people who have an appreciation for that.

DATE:

How I'm Embracing My Perfectly Imperfect Self Today:

LEVEL OF SELF-ACCEPTANCE TODAY:

☐ **A-** ☐ **A** ☐ **A+** ☐ **A++**

I am not eccentric. It's just that I am more alive than most people. I am an unpopular electric eel set in a pond of goldfish.

DATE:

How I'm Embracing My Perfectly Imperfect Self Today:

LEVEL OF SELF-ACCEPTANCE TODAY:

☐ A-　☐ A　☐ A+　☐ A++

Growth begins when we start to accept our own weakness.

Jean Vanier

DATE:

How I'm Embracing My Perfectly Imperfect Self Today:

LEVEL OF SELF-ACCEPTANCE TODAY:

☐ A- ☐ A ☐ A+ ☐ A++

So sensitive, said a family friend, that she could feel the grass grow under her feet.

DATE:

How I'm Embracing My Perfectly Imperfect Self Today:

LEVEL OF SELF-ACCEPTANCE TODAY:

☐ A- ☐ A ☐ A+ ☐ A++

I've done it all, and I've loved every trashy minute of it.

DATE:

How I'm Embracing My Perfectly Imperfect Self Today:

LEVEL OF SELF-ACCEPTANCE TODAY:

☐ A- ☐ A ☐ A+ ☐ A++

We don't have to wait until we are on our deathbed to realize what a waste of our precious lives it is to carry the belief that something is wrong with us.

DATE:

How I'm Embracing My Perfectly Imperfect Self Today:

LEVEL OF SELF-ACCEPTANCE TODAY:

☐ A- ☐ A ☐ A+ ☐ A++

Oh, never mind the fashion. When one has a style of one's own, it is always twenty times better.

DATE:

How I'm Embracing My Perfectly Imperfect Self Today:

LEVEL OF SELF-ACCEPTANCE TODAY:

☐ A- ☐ A ☐ A+ ☐ A++

There's not a thing wrong with you, you're right all the way through.

DATE:

How I'm Embracing My Perfectly Imperfect Self Today:

LEVEL OF SELF-ACCEPTANCE TODAY:

☐ A- ☐ A ☐ A+ ☐ A++

I told the doctor I was overtired, anxiety-ridden, compulsively active, constantly depressed, with recurring fits of paranoia. Turns out I'm normal.

DATE:

How I'm Embracing My Perfectly Imperfect Self Today:

LEVEL OF SELF-ACCEPTANCE TODAY:

☐ A- ☐ A ☐ A+ ☐ A++

You are already naked. There is no reason not to follow your heart.

DATE:

How I'm Embracing My Perfectly Imperfect Self Today:

LEVEL OF SELF-ACCEPTANCE TODAY:

☐ A- ☐ A ☐ A+ ☐ A++

For once, you believed in yourself. You believed you were beautiful and so did the rest of the world.

DATE:

How I'm Embracing My Perfectly Imperfect Self Today:

LEVEL OF SELF-ACCEPTANCE TODAY:

☐ A- ☐ A ☐ A+ ☐ A++

You are a child of the universe no less than the trees and the stars; you have a right to be here.

DATE:

How I'm Embracing My Perfectly Imperfect Self Today:

LEVEL OF SELF-ACCEPTANCE TODAY:

☐ A- ☐ A ☐ A+ ☐ A++

Eh, everybody makes mistakes. That's why they put erasers on pencils!

DATE:

How I'm Embracing My Perfectly Imperfect Self Today:

LEVEL OF SELF-ACCEPTANCE TODAY:

☐ A- ☐ A ☐ A+ ☐ A++

There will always be people who are much better at doing this or doing that—but you are the only you.

DATE:

How I'm Embracing My Perfectly Imperfect Self Today:

LEVEL OF SELF-ACCEPTANCE TODAY:

☐ A- ☐ A ☐ A+ ☐ A++

We love you.
Just as you are.

Knock Knock